Disney · PIXAR

ANNUAL 2007

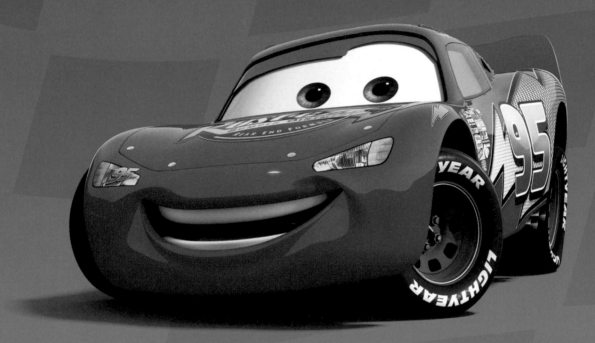

Editor: Jaine Keskeys
Art Editor: Phil Williams

EGMONT
We bring stories to life

First published in Great Britain in 2006
by Egmont UK Limited
239 Kensington High Street, London W8 6SA
© Disney Enterprises, Inc./Pixar Animation Studios

Disney/Pixar elements ©Disney/Pixar; Dodge®; Hudson Hornet™; ©Volkswagen AG; Hummer®; Model T™; Fiat™; Mack®; Mazda Miata®; Kenworth®; Chevrolet®; Peterbilt®; Porsche®; Jeep®; Mercury™; Plymouth Superbird™; Cadillac®; Ferrari®; Fairlane™; Petty®

The term OMNIDROID used by permission of Lucasfilm Ltd.

Note to parents: adult supervision is recommended when sharp-pointed items, such as scissors, are in use.

ISBN 978 1 4052 2602 8
ISBN 1 4052 2602 1
1 3 5 7 9 10 8 6 4 2
Printed in Italy

This book belongs to:

Name:  Jack

Age: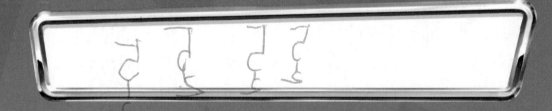

My favourite character is:

 Herbie.

CONTENTS

MONSTERS, INC.

TOY STORY AND BEYOND!

Doc's dare

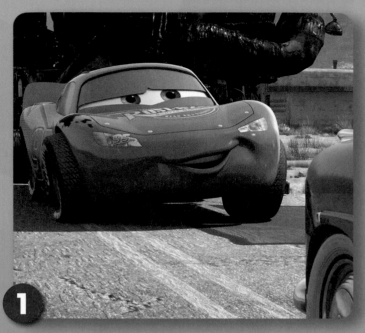

1

One day, Lightning McQueen accidentally arrived in Radiator Springs and tore up the main road. The residents were not impressed.

2

Doc Hudson dared McQueen to a race. If McQueen won then he could leave straight away but if he lost then he must first repair the road.

3

McQueen wasn't worried. After all, Doc was an old car and no match for him! McQueen was eager to leave the town, so he accepted Doc's dare.

4

The whole town of Radiator Springs turned up to watch the big race. They were waiting to cheer on both Doc and McQueen.

5

Excited Luigi waved the flag and started the race. McQueen immediately sped away in a cloud of dust, with his tyres screeching.

6

Doc was left at the starting line. He hadn't moved a wheel but he didn't even seem worried! Doc just watched, as McQueen drove into the distance.

7

Unaware that Doc wasn't following him, McQueen raced around the dirt track. It wasn't a smooth surface, like the ones he was used to racing on.

8

In fact, McQueen could feel his tyres sliding beneath him. As he turned a corner, he skidded on some loose rocks and lost control.

McQueen slid off the track and straight down a very steep hill. He landed in a prickly cactus patch. Ouch, it really hurt his tyres!

Meanwhile, Doc had been watching and waiting. He asked Mater to give McQueen a helping hand, by towing him back up the hill.

McQueen was not happy! It wasn't just his tyres that were hurt – his pride was, too. He couldn't stand losing, especially to an old car like Doc.

Finally, Doc revealed his big secret. He used to be a Champion race car himself! McQueen had to laugh, as he began to repair the road he'd ruined.

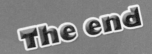
The end

Speedy shadows

The residents of Radiator Springs are out for a spin on Route 66. Can you match the cars to their shadows?

Luigi

... is a 1959 Italian-made sports car.

Fillmore

... is a 1960s van.

Sarge

... is a 1942 WWII vehicle.

Flo

... is a 1950s show car.

Sheriff

... is a 1949 black-and-white police cruiser.

a

b

c

d

e

Answer: Luigi – d, Fillmore – e, Sarge – a, Flo – c, Sheriff – b.

11

Pulling puzzle

Can you follow Mater's three tow ropes, to find out which car is being towed by each rope?

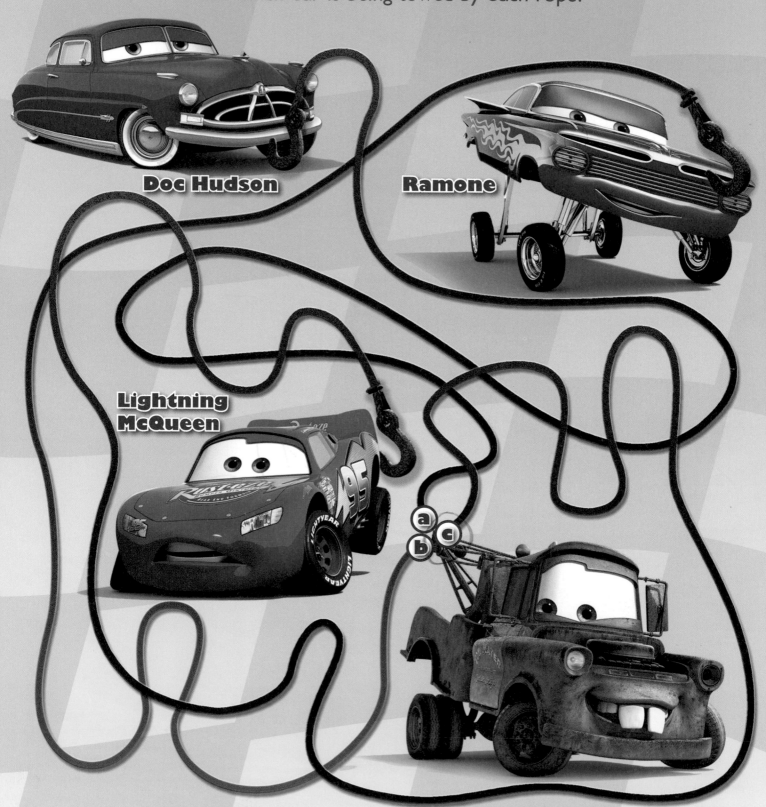

Doc Hudson

Ramone

Lightning McQueen

12

Cool colours

McQueen is almost ready to race! Give him some winning colours, using the small picture to help you.

Racing route

Will you win the Piston Cup?
Find out in this roaring race game!

You will need:
- A colourful counter for each player!
- A dice.

How to play:
- Place all the counters at the Start line. Throw a dice, to see who gets pole position and starts first.
- Take it in turns to throw the dice and then move the counters around the track.
- If you land on a coloured shield or a purple flash, follow the instruction.
- The first player to cross the Finish line is the winner. Who will come in second and third positions, too?

START

FINISH

Hit by another car – miss a go

Lots of fuel left – take an extra turn

Finish line is close – take an extra turn

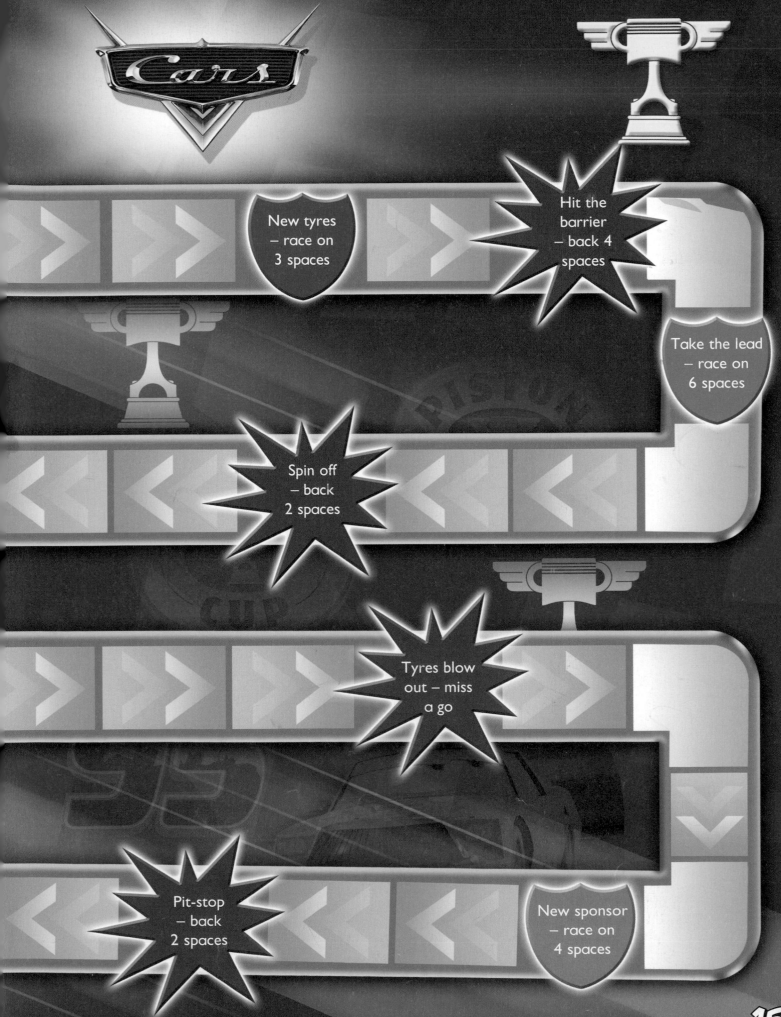

New tyres – race on 3 spaces

Hit the barrier – back 4 spaces

Take the lead – race on 6 spaces

Spin off – back 2 spaces

Tyres blow out – miss a go

Pit-stop – back 2 spaces

New sponsor – race on 4 spaces

15

Mater's mischief

Mater and McQueen are tractor tipping and making mischief! Can you spot 8 differences in the bottom picture?

Answers: 1) McQueen's rear spoiler is missing. 2) Mater's hook has moved. 3) Mater's eyes have moved. 4) Mater's tooth is missing. 5) McQueen's 95 is a different colour. 6) A tyre is missing. 7) Tractor's chimney is missing. 8) Tractor's wheel is missing.

Pick a pattern

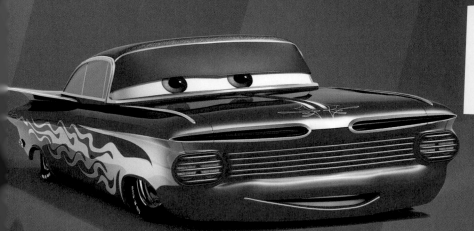

Ramone resprays himself every day, so he needs some new ideas! Create and colour your own designs on the cars below.

The big race

Thousands of cars gathered to watch the biggest race of the year and cheer on their favourite racers. The winner would take home the Piston Cup.

Lightning McQueen, The King and Chick all had equal points. So, would the winner be rookie race car Lightning McQueen? Would The King, who was about to retire, win his last race? Or would Chick finally win, after so many runner-up positions?

McQueen had already won many trophies and wanted to add the Piston Cup to his collection!

McQueen, The King and Chick lined up. They waited for the signal and then they were off! Tyres screeched and engines roared, as the cars sped round the track.

It was a fast and furious race, with the lead position changing several times during the first few laps. It was going to be close! Chick would do anything to win, even if it meant cheating. So, as the racers rounded a tight corner, he rammed into another car. The car spun out of control, hitting other cars. The pile-up blocked the track.

18

Chick carried on racing, sure that McQueen would now be out of the race.

The crowd all cheered, as McQueen emerged from the wreckage, without even a scratch! He passed a shocked Chick and took the lead. Surely nobody could stop him!

McQueen made a pit stop to refuel. His team wanted to change his tyres but McQueen refused. He made the quickest pit stop on record and kept ahead of Chick and The King.

The finish line was in sight and McQueen raced towards it.

Suddenly, he felt one of his back tyres burst. McQueen didn't panic – he could still make it to the finish line. Then his other back tyre burst, too! Now he was in trouble. McQueen struggled towards the finish line. He was going so slowly that The King and Chick caught up with him and they all crossed the line together. It was a photo finish!

Everyone waited nervously for the result. It was a three-way tie and so another race would be held. Which car would win and finally take home the Piston Cup?

The end

Cool cup

Make this cool winner's cup and give it pride of place in your bedroom. Doc Hudson still has all his cups!

1 Cover a paper cup in kitchen foil. Cut another paper cup in half, as shown. Paint the bottom half black.

2 When the paint is dry, stick the bottom of the black cup on to the bottom of the silver cup.

3 Cut two strips of card and cover them in kitchen foil. Bend the strips and stick them on to the silver cup, to make handles.

20

Note to parents: adult supervision is recommended when scissors are in use.

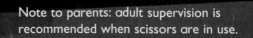

Write your name on a piece of paper and stick it on to the black cup, to show that you raced in to first place!

Lightning McQueen

Colouring fun

22

Close-up McQueen

Look closely at the big picture of McQueen. Can you see which one of the close-ups at the bottom is not of him?

Answer: Close-up d.

23

Fishy funfair

1

One day, Nemo and his friends saw a crowd of fish, gathered on the reef. "I wonder what's going on?" puzzled Pearl. "Let's have a look," said Nemo.

2

So they all swam off towards the crowd. When they got closer, they saw that it was a funfair, full of fun rides, great games and yummy food!

3

They were very excited. "What shall we have a go on first?" asked Nemo. "The Crab Carts!" cried Tad. "They look too fast for me!" said Pearl.

4

"Why don't we get some coral candy?" suggested Pearl. Nemo and Tad thought it was a great idea and soon they were all munching on the pink coral candy.

Suddenly, a mean-looking electric eel snatched Pearl's coral candy. "Hey! Give that back!" cried Pearl. The nasty eel laughed at her and swam away.

"Boo hoo!" sobbed Pearl. "Don't worry, we'll get it back for you," said Tad. The three friends swam off after the eel, to retrieve Pearl's coral candy.

The eel had pushed in front of the other fish at the Octo-Whirl ride. He was about to get in one of the eight carriages. "What now?" asked Tad.

"I know!" said Nemo. He spoke to the octopus in charge of the ride. When Nemo told the octopus about the coral candy, he agreed to help them.

9

10

The octopus started to spin, really fast. He spun so fast that the eel dropped the coral candy. "Hooray!" cheered Pearl, as she reached up to catch it.

When the ride stopped, the eel was very dizzy and swam away in circles. "Thanks, Mr Octopus!" cried Pearl, as they swam off to enjoy the funfair.

About the story

1) Which ride did Tad want to go on first?
2) What colour was the coral candy?
3) What type of eel stole Pearl's candy?
4) How many carriages were on the Octo-Whirl?

Answers:
1) The Crab Carts. 2) Pink. 3) An electric eel. 4) Eight.

26

Colour Crush

Can you add some bright colours to Crush and his friends?

Pearl finger-puppet

For some fabulously fishy fun, why not make this great Pearl finger-puppet? Here's how!

You will need: White card, a black pen, scissors and purple paint.

1 Draw a picture of Pearl on some white card.

2 Cut out Pearl and then draw four circles along the bottom. They must be large enough for your fingers to fit through.

Note to parents: adult supervision is recommended when scissors are in use.

3 Next, carefully cut out the finger-holes.

4 Finally, paint Pearl purple!

Did you know that octopuses have eight legs?

29

Crab questions

Marlin and Dory have bumped into some grumpy crabs. That won't stop them from having some fun with you, though!

1 How many crabs can you count?

2 Which crab is the odd one out?

3 Which detail below does not appear in the main picture?

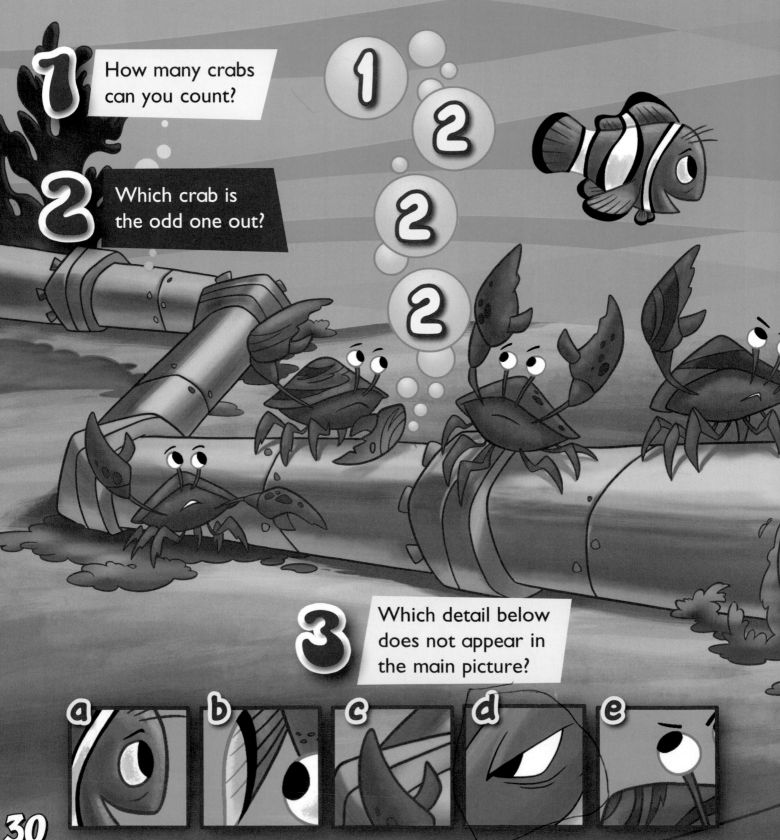

a b c d e

31

Tank teaser

Although Deb and Flo look exactly the same, their surroundings don't. Can you find ten differences in the reflection on the right?

Answers:

1) The top sail is missing. 2) The treasure chest is open. 3) There is less seaweed under Flo. 4) The barrel isn't broken. 5) The helmet has no grill. 6) There is no oyster pearl. 7) There is no crow's nest. 8) The bubbles above Flo are missing. 9) The rigging is a different colour. 10) There is no lava.

Find the fish

Try to find the five fish below in the jellyfish jumble, ticking the boxes when you spot them. Which fish is not in the jumble?

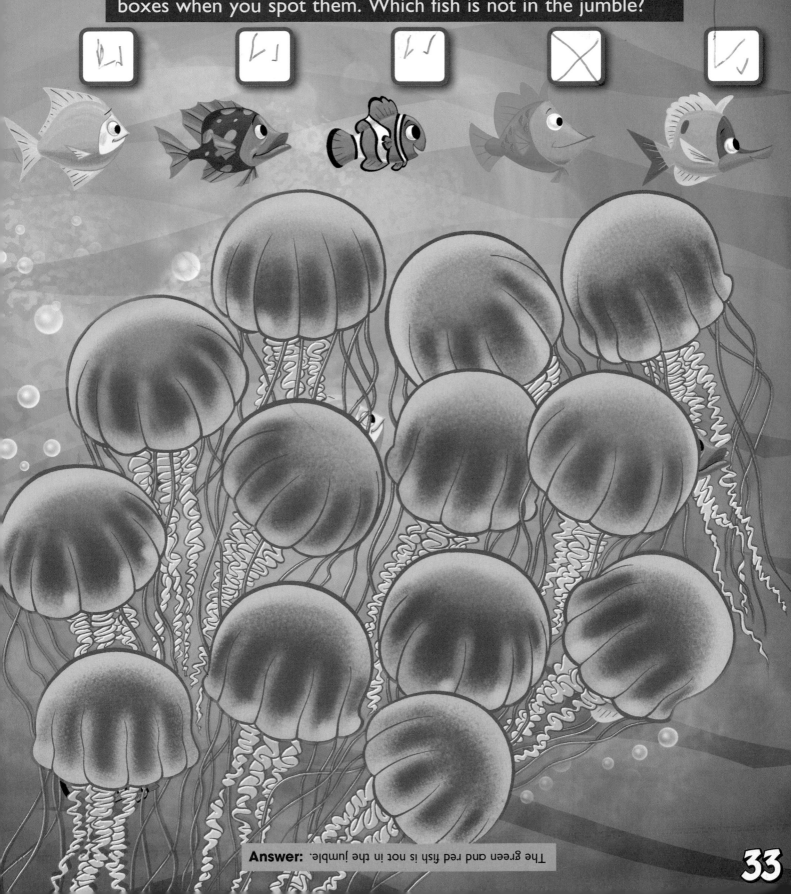

33

The big bully

It's tough being little if there's no one big to stand up for you. Marlin and Nemo know how to handle a big bully, though!

One day, Nemo and Marlin were playing by the coral, when the ocean suddenly went very quiet.

Then from out of the murky waters, a big barracuda came darting straight towards them.

"Look out, Dad!" cried Nemo. The two little clownfish dodged the hungry barracuda and swam into some sea anemones.

"We're safe in here. I wish that big bully would leave us alone," gulped Marlin.

Just then, a baby shark came swimming along. The barracuda was much bigger than the little shark and decided to chase him.

The baby shark was very scared. He was just about to get caught, when the barracuda stopped.

The baby shark's huge father had come to look for him. The barracuda knew he was no match for such a big fish, so he swam away.

It was finally safe for Nemo and Marlin to come out of hiding. "Wow! That bully won't bother that baby shark again. I wish we could scare him like that," said Nemo.

"Sharks grow big but clownfish stay small. The barracuda knows there's no one big in our family to chase him away," sighed Marlin.

Nemo didn't think it was fair. He flicked the sea bed with his tail and a cloud of orange dust flew up and settled on a shell.

"Hey, look at the colour of that shell! It looks totally different now," said Nemo, amazed.

Marlin looked at the shell and had an idea. "Nemo, you're a genius! I think we should find one of our old friends!" he exclaimed.

The next day, Nemo and Marlin were playing in the same place, when the ocean went silent again.

"I think that bully is back," said Marlin. The barracuda appeared from the darkness, heading for them. This time, they didn't swim away in fear.

Suddenly, a giant clownfish with very sharp teeth, rose up in front of the barracuda. "Go away!" boomed the big clownfish. The barracuda almost broke his fin trying to swim away!

When he was gone, Marlin, Nemo and the giant clownfish all started to laugh. As the giant clownfish's huge body shook, his orange and white markings began to billow off.

Nemo and Marlin had covered Bruce the shark with dust! "I don't think that bully will mess with clownfish from now on!" laughed Bruce.

The end

35

Shade the shark

Bruce the shark doesn't scare chatty Dory! Can you add some colours to this scene?

Nemo's jigsaws

Help Nemo complete these two jigsaws, by writing the correct letter in each empty space.

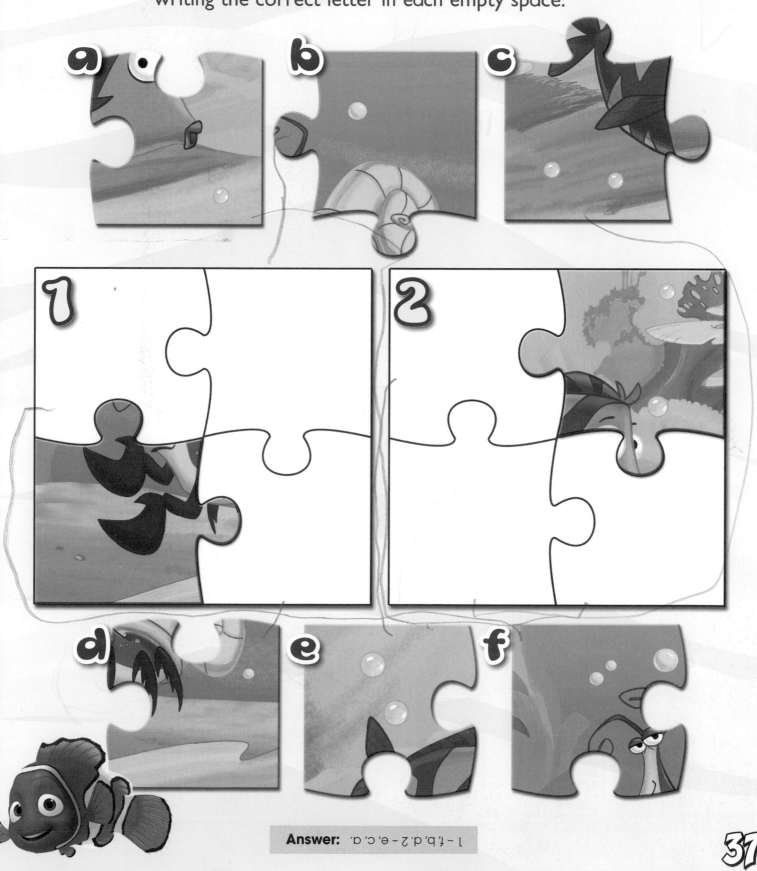

37

Incredible battle

The Incredibles and Frozone have teamed up to fight this Omnidroid. Answer these questions while they do battle!

1 What do the numbers in Frozone's ice path add up to?

4 1 3 2

2 Which little picture below is not in the main picture?

a   b   c   d   e   f

3 How many legs does this Omnidroid have? `5`

4 Which of these three mixed-up words correctly spells Omnidroid?

1 niddriom
2 droioimnd
3 moidrooid

5 Can you see which piece completes Violet's force field?

a
b
c
d

39

Vanishing Violet

Make Violet visible again! Finish and colour the drawing, using the picture on the right to help you.

VIOLET

Super close-ups

Can you work out who Syndrome is spying on each time?
Use the faces down the side of the page to help you.

a

b

c

d

e

Mr. Incredible

Elastigirl

Violet

Jack-Jack

Dash

Answers:
a - Elastigirl, b - Mr. Incredible,
c - Jack-Jack, d - Violet, e - Dash.

41

Colour challenge

Will you and a friend dare to become Mr. Incredible and Syndrome, as they battle it out in this Super-exciting and explosive game?

You will need: Coloured pens and a dice.

How to play

Decide which character each player will be, by throwing the dice. Whoever throws the highest number will be Mr. Incredible. Next, take it in turns to throw the dice. Colour in one of your sections that matches the number you throw. Miss a go if you have coloured all of your sections that match the number thrown. The first player to colour in their character wins but BEWARE! If you colour all three of your explosions before your character is complete, the other player wins!

A Super slice

1 One day, Dash and Violet came home from school, to find that someone had left a last slice of cake on the table in the dining room. Their eyes lit up!

2 Dash and Violet grinned at each other, knowing that only one of them could have it. "It's mine!" yelled Violet, as Dash grabbed the slice of cake.

3 Violet threw a force field in front of Dash, who ran into it at full speed. The cake flew out of his hand. Violet then chased Dash down the hall.

4 The cake sailed through the air and landed back on the plate. Then, Bob walked into the dining room. "I should be watching my weight!" he chuckled.

5

Bob took the cake and walked into the front room, where he stepped on Jack-Jack's toy train. Bob fell, letting go of the cake.

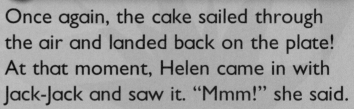

6

Once again, the cake sailed through the air and landed back on the plate! At that moment, Helen came in with Jack-Jack and saw it. "Mmm!" she said.

7

Helen put Jack-Jack in his highchair and was about to taste the cake, when she heard Bob groaning. She put down the cake and went to help him.

8

Dash ran into the front room, followed by Violet. "The last slice is mine!" they both yelled. "Yours? I was going to have it!" cried Bob and Helen.

9

10

"Well, perhaps we can all share it?" suggested Helen. They all gasped, as lumps of cake suddenly came splattering from the dining room.

They were too late! "Look, Jack-Jack's got the last slice!" cried Dash. "Well, at least he's sharing it with us!" laughed Bob.

The end

About the story

1) Why did Dash let go of the last slice?
2) What did Bob step on?
3) Who went to help Bob?
4) Which Incredible did get the last slice in the end?

Answers:
1) He ran into Violet's force field. 2) Jack-Jack's toy train. 3) Helen. 4) Jack-Jack.

Dash's dash

Can you help Dash race through the cave to escape from Syndrome's guards?

Start

Finish

47

Mike's bright idea

1

2

One day, Mr Waternoose said there was to be a new advertising campaign. "We need someone to be the new face of Monsters, Inc.," he explained.

Mike really liked the idea of being famous, so he rushed forward to volunteer. "Pick me, pick me!" he cried. Mike couldn't wait to start!

3

4

"They might use my face on posters, or put me in a TV advert!" Mike giggled. However, when he found out what he had to do, he wasn't so excited.

Mr Waternoose gave Mike a big stack of leaflets. "Start by handing these out," he said. When Mike stood on the street corner, everyone ignored him!

5 Mike was getting tired and was about to give up, when he saw a big crowd chasing a young monster's stray balloon. He decided to help.

6 Mike caught the balloon and gave it to the young monster. "Thanks. Hey, you look just like my balloon!" he giggled. Mike looked at the balloon and smiled.

7 He ran back and told Mr Waternoose that he knew a way to advertise Monsters, Inc. all over the city. "Let's give it a go," Mr Waternoose said.

8 Mike painted balloons to look just like him! They floated all over the city of Monstropolis. "Now, no one can ignore Monsters, Inc., or me!" he chuckled.

The end

49

Canister count

It's scare time for Sulley! Which path should he take in order to fill the most scream canisters?

a b c d e

Answer: Path d (6 canisters).

50

Monster mix-up

Can you work out who owns each of these Monsters, Inc. ID cards? Read the description, then write in the correct monster number.

1

MONSTERS, INC.

Blue with big teeth

2

MONSTERS, INC.

Pink with lots of eyes

3

MONSTERS, INC.

Furry with one horn

4

MONSTERS, INC.

Green with one eye

5

MONSTERS, INC.

Scaly with a wide mouth

6

MONSTERS, INC.

Furry with two horns

a **b** **c** **d** **e** **f**

51

Sulley sign

Mark your territory with this fun, furry door sign!

You will need: Blue card, paints, scissors, glue, blue and purple wool and a marker pen.

1 Draw Sulley's head, with his mouth wide open, on some blue card.

2 Paint the details on and then cut out Sulley's head.

3 Spread glue over the blue part of Sulley's face, except for inside his mouth.

Note to parents: adult supervision is recommended when scissors are in use.

4 Cut some blue and purple wool into small pieces. Stick them on to the glued area.

5 With a marker pen, write your name inside Sulley's mouth. Finally, stick the sign on your bedroom door!

WILL YOUR SIGN SCARE PEOPLE AWAY?

Sulley

Sulley

Puzzle page

Sulley is visiting his little friend, Boo. Join them as they have some monster-sized fun!

1 How many flowers are on Boo's bedroom door?

2 What colour is the bow on Sulley's horn?

m
o
n
s
t
e
r

3 What mighty word is written on Boo's building blocks?

4 Which monster has Boo drawn a picture of?

5 Who is peeking around the door?

6 What do the numbers on the ducks add up to?

55

Little monsters

Can you shower these mini-monsters with bright colours?

56

Which door?

Can you work out each monster's sum, to see which door they should go through? Draw a line to join each monster to its door.

12

8

14

7

10

George

2×5

Ricky

7+7

Randall

4+3

Bile

10-2

6×2

Sulley

57

Super Slinky

1

One day, Andy and his mum went out for the day. "We've got the house to ourselves!" cheered Woody. "Now we can go really wild," giggled Rex.

2

Rex roared and chased Woody around the room. Woody ran straight into Slinky, who was stretched out across the floor, and landed in a heap.

3

"Oops! Sorry, I didn't see you there," said Slinky. Slinky then turned around and his tail end knocked straight into Rex. "Oops! Sorry again!" said Slinky.

4

"Your crazy spring is such a menace. It's always causing problems!" said Rex. Slinky felt really bad and so he tried to keep out of their way.

58

5

Later, Rex was chasing Woody over the desk, when they accidentally knocked one of Andy's school books out of the window. "Oh, no!" said Rex.

6

"We must get it back, or Andy will wonder where his homework's gone!" cried Woody. "It's starting to rain. The book will be ruined!" gasped Rex.

7

Suddenly, Slinky ran across the room. "Hold on to my tail!" he yelled, diving out of the window. Slinky's spring stretched right down to the ground.

8

Slinky then bounced back up into the room with the book in his mouth. "Your crazy spring can solve problems, too!" laughed Woody and Rex.

The end

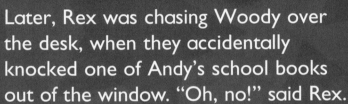

Let's dance!

Howdy, partner! Here are some rootin' tootin' teasers for you to tackle, while Woody and Jessie show Buzz their cowboy moves.

1 Who is spinning a lasso?

2 Which little picture does not appear in the big picture?

3 Is Woody standing on his right or left leg?

a   b   c   d   e   f

4 Can you find four five-pointed star shapes hidden in the picture?

5 Who is dancing in the middle?

6 How many records does Rex have?

61

Next in line

The faces in each row follow a pattern. Can you work out who should be in each empty square?

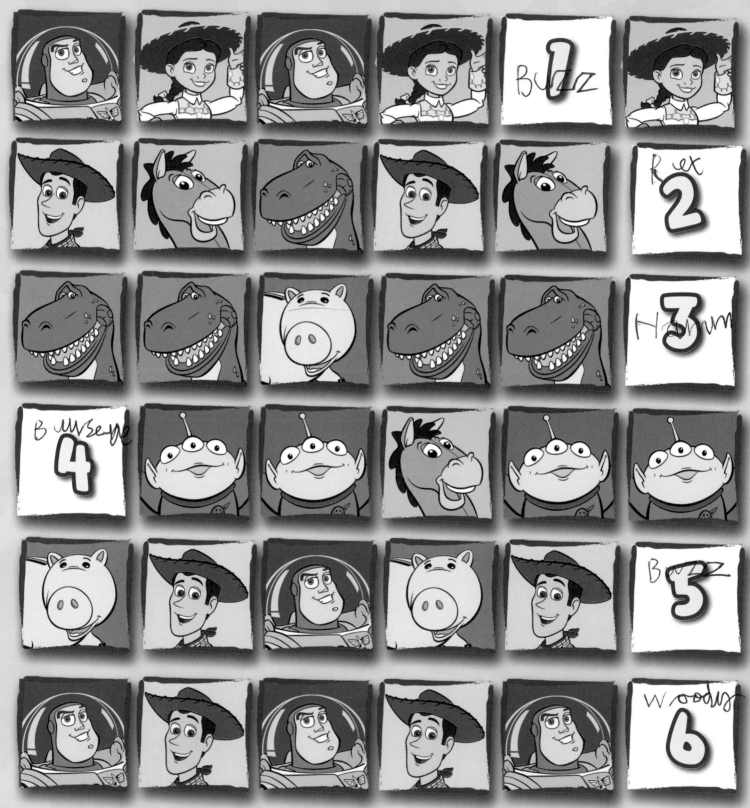

Answers: 1) Buzz, 2) Rex, 3) Hamm, 4) Bullseye, 5) Buzz, 6) Woody.

Draw the dog

Trace over the lines and then give Woody and Buster some cowboy colours!

Forward march

Andy has left his little green army men all around his room. Play this game with a friend, to see who can find five of them first!

You will need: A dice, a counter for each player and some tokens to use as soldiers.

Start

How to play

Put all the green army men tokens to one side and place each player's counter on Start. Take it in turns to roll the dice and move your counter around the board. Every time you land on a green army man, take one token. The first player to collect five tokens is the winner!

Toy teasers

The toys are ready to have some fun. Why don't you join them?

1 Who is next to Buzz and also above Jessie?

2 Which add up to the most, the numbers on the jigsaw pieces, or the numbers on the balls?

3 How many alien shadows can you find on this page?

66

Rex's Race

Can you help Rex race through this maze from
Start to Finish, collecting every toy along the way?

Start

Finish

Quick questions

Before you go, answer these quick questions about your Annual!

1 What happened to Lightning McQueen when he raced Doc Hudson?

He fell into a patch of caterpil

2 On which page did this tractor appear?

16

3 How many fish were hiding on page 33?

4

4 Who was sliding on to page 38?

Dash Frozone!

5 On which page did this boy appear?

50

6 Who was racing on page 67?

Rex